Slime Club

JENNIFER B. STITH

See the clock?

It is time for
slime club!

My pals are here to make slime with me.

Get a glass dish.

Get the glue.

Mix in some bling to
make it glam.

Take some slime.

Make a blob.

Flip and flop it.

Make it long.

Slime club is
so much fun!